About the Book

The stories of the Bible have a timeless appeal for children and adults alike. Handed down from generation to generation for centuries, the stories of Noah, David and Goliath, Samson, Esther, and Daniel have held listeners spellbound.

This collection of Bible stories, retold simply and beautifully by Alvin Tresselt and illustrated by Caldecott Award winning artist Lynd Ward, is a fine introduction for children into the rich tradition of the Old Testament. Alvin Tresselt's text is dignified, yet dramatically powerful. Lynd Ward's stunning full-page lithographs will leave unforgettable visual impressions of the colorful times and the striking figures the stories bring so vividly to life.

A distinguished author and artist have collaborated to make this handsome volume of STORIES FROM THE BIBLE a classic to be treasured.

STORIES
FROM THE
BIBLE

STORIES FROM THE BIBLE

retold by
Alvin Tresselt

with lithographs by
Lynd Ward

Coward, McCann & Geoghegan, Inc.
New York

CONTENTS

THE TWENTY-FOURTH PSALM

THE EARTH IS THE LORD's and the fulness thereof,
The world, and they that dwell therein;
For He hath founded it upon the sea,
And established it upon the floods.

NOAH

For thousands of years the stories of the Bible have been told and retold. Scholars have studied them, and children all over the world have loved them. The Bible has been translated into almost every language. Here are some of the great stories from the Old Testament — stories of good and righteous men who walked with God and loved Him; of brave men who led the Lord's people to victory over their enemies; of fearless women who served the Lord faithfully.

The first of these righteous men is Noah, a man chosen by God to live through the days and nights of the great flood which covered the earth.

I N THE EARLY DAYS of the world the hearts of men had grown hard and full of wickedness. Men turned from the ways of the Lord, and the Lord, seeing these things, was not pleased.

"I shall destroy every living thing I have made," said the Lord, "and man whom I have created. Every living creature on the face of the earth shall I wipe out, for man is evil in my sight."

But there was one man who remembered the ways of the Lord. Noah and his three sons, Shem, Ham, and Japheth, rejoiced in the Lord, and their prayers were heard in heaven. And so the Lord spoke to Noah, saying, "In my wrath shall I destroy every living thing. But you of all men have found favor in my eyes. Therefore, I will spare you and your children.

"Build of stout wood from the forests an ark, a boat, for I shall cover the earth with a great flood of waters. Into the ark shall you gather two of every living creature, every beast and everything that creeps or crawls on the land or flies in the air, both male and female. Take also into the ark food of every kind so that all may eat while the waters cover the land."

And Noah did as the Lord had commanded. Of gopher wood he and his sons built the ark. Then he gathered together two animals of every kind. All things that breathed the breath of life did he gather into the ark. When the rains came, Noah and his sons and their wives went up into the ark, and the Lord closed the great door against the waters.

Then the Lord caused the rains to fall. The windows of heaven were opened up, and the fountains of the deep were broken. For forty days and forty nights the rains fell, and the earth was covered, even to the tops of high hills and mountains. And the ark went out upon the face of the waters. Every living thing that breathed was destroyed, and the water remained upon the earth for one hundred and fifty days.

Then the Lord remembered Noah. He caused a wind to pass over the waters, and the flood began to go down. In the seventh month the ark rested upon the mountains of Ararat.

Noah opened the window of the ark and sent forth a dove to find if the waters had left the face of the earth, but the dove

returned, for she had found no place to rest the sole of her foot. For seven days Noah waited. Then he sent forth the dove again, and in the evening she returned with a green olive leaf. Again for seven days did Noah wait. Once more he opened the window of the ark and sent forth the dove, but in the evening she did not return. So at last Noah knew that the waters had left the face of the earth. He opened the great door of the ark and looked out. Behold, the land was dry. Then at the Lord's command out from the ark went every living thing, every beast and all the birds of the air. Noah built an altar and offered up burnt sacrifices and praise to the Lord who had spared the earth from destruction.

The Lord was well pleased and spoke to Noah and his sons, saying, "Behold, I give you my covenant — my promise — to you and your children and your children's children unto the end of the earth, and to all living creatures, the birds and the cattle and every beast that creeps or crawls. While the earth remains, there shall be seedtime and harvest, cold and heat, summer and winter, and day and night shall not cease.

"When the clouds gather over the earth to bring forth rain, my bow will appear and I will remember my promise to you and all living creatures. Never again shall the waters become a flood to destroy the earth."

ABRAHAM

Abraham was the first great leader of the Hebrew people. In the days when men worshiped many gods, Abraham led his people in the ways of the one God of heaven and earth.

IN THE LAND OF UR lived a man named Abram. The people of Ur had many gods. They made idols of their gods, and they worshiped them. But with all his heart Abram loved and feared the one Lord God. And the Lord appeared to Abram and said, "Leave your land, your people and your father's home for a land I will show you. I will make you the founder of a great nation and I will make your name great among men. I will bless those who bless you, and I will curse those who curse you."

And Abram did as the Lord commanded. With his wife, Sarai, and his herds of cattle and camels he set out for the land of Canaan, which the Lord had promised to him and his descendants. The years passed, and Abram prospered in the sight of the Lord. His flocks grew in number, and also his cattle. But his wife could bear him no children.

Then the Lord spoke to Abram and said, "Look to the sky and count the stars if you can. To such a number shall your children's children grow, even to the end of time. And your name shall be Abraham, father of nations, and your wife shall be called Sarah, for she will be the mother of nations."

And it came to pass that as Abraham sat at the tent door in the heat of the day, three men stood near him, and he ran to meet them. They were strangers, but Abraham knew in his heart that they were messengers of the Lord. He bowed low before them, saying, "Rest here in the shade of the tree, and I will fetch water so that your feet may be bathed."

Then Abraham hastened to Sarah and said, "Make fine bread while I kill and prepare a calf, and thus we will have food for our guests."

While the strangers ate and rested, one of the men questioned Abraham, saying, "Where is Sarah, your wife?"

And Abraham said, "She stands there — in the tent."

The man replied, "Lo, she shall bear you a son."

Now Sarah was listening in the tent door behind him, and she laughed to herself and said, "How shall I bear a son now that I am so old?"

Then the messenger said to Abraham, "Why does Sarah laugh and say, 'How shall I bear a son now that I am old?' Is anything too hard for the Lord to make possible?"

So it was as the Lord said. In her old age Sarah bore Abraham a son. And they named the child Isaac, which means laughter.

Thus through his son, Isaac, and Isaac's sons and grandsons, Abraham became the father of multitudes and Sarah the mother of nations.

ISAAC

In the days when Isaac lived, it was the custom for the fathers to choose wives for their sons. Now since Abraham was a very old man by the time Isaac was ready to marry, he entrusted the task to a faithful servant. This, then, is the story of how Isaac's marriage came about.

THE YEARS PASSED, and Isaac grew to manhood. Abraham was old, and the Lord had blessed him in all things. He commanded his eldest and most trusted servant to come before him, saying, "I have made a covenant with my God that my son will not marry one of the Canaanites, among whom we dwell. Go, then, to the land of my people and of my fathers, and seek there for a wife for Isaac."

And the servant answered, "But what shall I do if the woman is not willing to follow me back to this country? Shall I then take your son back to the land from which you came?"

Abraham said to him, "Swear that you will never take my

son there. This is the land which the Lord God has given to me and my children's children. Here shall they live forever. The angel of the Lord will guide your footsteps. Have no fear."

Then the servant gathered together ten camels for the journey and gifts of fine gold and treasures for the bride. And he set out for the land of Abraham's people. When he came to the city of Nahor, it was evening, and he stopped beside a well of water, making the camels kneel down beside the well. And it was the time of day when the women of the city came to draw water.

The servant of Abraham prayed to God, saying, "Now are the women come to the well. To one I shall say, 'Let down your pitcher that I may drink.' If she be the wife You have chosen for Isaac, let her say, 'Drink, and I will give your camels water also.' Then will I know that You have shown kindness to my master, Abraham."

While he was still praying, Rebekah came to the well. Her father was the son of Nahor, Abraham's brother. She was very fair, and when she had filled her pitcher, the servant ran to meet her, saying, "Let down your pitcher so that I may drink."

"Drink, my lord," she said. And when he had finished drinking, she said, "I will draw water for your camels also." Then she filled the trough beside the well with water from her pitcher until the camels had finished drinking.

The servant said nothing until the camels were done; then he offered Rebekah a golden earring and two bracelets of heavy rich gold for her hands. "Whose daughter are you," he asked, "and is there room in your father's house for me and my camels?"

When she told him her father's name, she said, "We have

both fodder for your camels and room for you." The servant praised God in his heart, for he knew he had chosen rightly.

Then Rebekah ran to her home and told of what had happened. Her brother, Laban, returned to the well so that he might bring the servant to his house and lodge the camels for the night. When food was set before the servant, he said, "I will not eat until I tell my story. I am the servant of Abraham, whom the Lord has blessed. He has both flocks and herds, silver and gold; also camels and many servants. Isaac is the son of his old age, and for love of his son he has given him all that he has."

And the servant told how Abraham had sent him to seek a bride for Isaac and how the Lord had led him to Rebekah.

Then Laban answered, saying, "This is how the Lord wills it. Here is Rebekah — take her and go. Let her be the wife of Abraham's son even as the Lord has said."

So it was that the servant brought Rebekah into the land of Canaan to be the wife of Isaac.

JOSEPH AND HIS BROTHERS

One of the sons of Isaac and Rebekah was Jacob, to whom the Lord gave the name Israel. Jacob had twelve sons, and from them came the twelve tribes of Israel. This is the story of Joseph, Jacob's favorite son, and what happened between him and his brothers.

THERE WAS IN THOSE DAYS a boy named Joseph, the beloved son of his father, Jacob. His ten older brothers were jealous when they saw their father favor Joseph, and they could not say a good word for the boy.

Now Jacob was troubled by all this, but he loved his son greatly, so he gave him a coat of many colors to show his love. And the brothers hated Joseph in their hearts.

One night Joseph dreamed a dream, and when he told it to his brothers, they hated him more. "I dreamed we were binding sheaves of grain in the field," he said. "My sheaf stood upright, and your sheaves gathered around mine and bowed down to it."

Then Joseph had still another dream, and he told his father and brothers, "I dreamed that the sun and moon and eleven stars bowed down to me."

Jacob rebuked him, saying, "What is this dream? Shall I and your mother and your brothers indeed come to bow down to

22

you?" And Joseph's ten older brothers envied him all the more.

It came to pass that the brothers were in a far-off place, tending their father's sheep. Jacob, wishing to know if all went well with his sons and his flocks, sent Joseph to find them, saying, "Go to your brothers and bring me word of how they fare at their work."

But when the brothers saw Joseph approach, wearing his many-colored coat, they plotted to kill him and cast him into a pit. Then on their return to their father's tents they would tell Jacob that a wild beast had devoured his son.

But Reuben spoke up and said, "Let us not have his blood on our hands. We will cast him into a pit to live or die as it might be."

And when Joseph approached them, they seized him and stripped him of his coat and threw him into a pit in the wilderness. But at that moment they spied a caravan of Ishmaelites with their camels, carrying spices and myrrh down to the land of Egypt. One of the brothers spoke, saying, "Let us not leave Joseph in the pit, but sell him as a slave to the traders so that he will be carried out of the land of Canaan."

And so it was. The brothers sold Joseph for twenty pieces of silver, and they took his coat and dipped it in the blood of a newly killed he-goat to show their father that Joseph had been slain by wild beasts. And Jacob was bowed with grief.

When at last the caravan arrived in Egypt, the traders sold Joseph to a man named Potiphar, the captain of Pharaoh's guard, and he served him well. Potiphar was pleased with Joseph, and he put him in charge of all that he had, both his fields and his house. But in time Joseph was unjustly accused of a crime, and he was thrown into prison.

Now it happened that the head butler and the head baker of the Pharaoh of Egypt had offended him, and they were also thrown into the prison where Joseph was. One night each of the men had a strange dream. The butler told Joseph, "I dreamed there was a vine with three branches that put forth blossoms, and the blossoms became three clusters of ripe grapes. These grapes did I press into Pharaoh's cup, and I gave it into his hand."

Joseph answered, saying that the three branches were three days and that after three days the butler would once more be serving Pharaoh his wine as he had done before.

Then the baker said, "I dreamed I had three white baskets on my head filled with cakes for Pharaoh, and the birds came and they ate the cakes from out of the top basket."

Joseph replied that the three baskets were three days and that after three days Pharaoh would cut off his head, and he would be hanged from a tree where the birds would devour him.

And so it was. In three days the butler was called back to the palace, but the baker was hanged. And Joseph spoke to the butler, saying, "Remember me when you serve Pharaoh and speak to him, for I am unjustly held in this prison." But the butler forgot Joseph.

It came to pass that at the end of two full years Pharaoh had two dreams, and all the wise men of Egypt could not explain the dreams of their king.

Then the butler remembered Joseph, and he approached Pharaoh and said, "There is in your prison house a young man, a Hebrew and servant of Potiphar, who has been unjustly accused of a crime. He has the power from his God to interpret dreams."

Pharaoh sent for Joseph at once and told him thus: "I dreamed that seven fat cows came up out of the river Nile and fed in the reed grass. Then seven lean and hungry cows came up out of the river and they ate the seven fat cows. Then I slept and dreamed a second time. Seven good ears of corn grew upon one stalk. Then seven lean ears, thin and blasted by the east wind, sprang up beside them. And the seven lean ears devoured the seven fat ears."

Joseph answered Pharaoh, saying, "God has shown Pharaoh what he is about to do. The seven fat cows and the seven good ears are seven years of plenty, and the seven lean cows and the seven lean ears are seven years of famine, when no food will grow in all the land. Therefore, let Pharaoh appoint a man to gather up the grain for seven years and store it away so that when the years of famine come, there will be food in the land of Egypt."

And Pharaoh said to Joseph, "Since your God has given you the power to read my dream, I will make you overseer of the land, second only to me in power. You will gather up the grain for seven years against the days of famine that will follow." He gave Joseph the ring from his hand and dressed him in fine linen and put a gold chain about his neck.

And it was as Joseph had said. For seven years the crops were rich and plentiful, and he gathered grain as the sands of the sea until he could count no more, so great was the number. Then the seven years of plenty came to an end, and the seven years of famine began. There was famine in all lands, even in the land of Canaan where dwelled Jacob and his sons.

Now Jacob heard that there was grain in Egypt, so he sent ten of his sons forth to buy grain so that they might live. But

Benjamin, the youngest, he kept by his side lest any harm should come to him.

When the brothers came before Joseph, he knew them, but they knew him not. Joseph spoke roughly to them, saying, "You are spies come from the land of Canaan to see the weakness of Egypt in its time of famine." But the brothers protested and said they were the sons of Jacob, who was at home with their youngest brother, Benjamin, and had come only to buy food. They bowed before him and begged that he believe them. Then Joseph remembered his dream, and he hid his head and wept so that they might not see him.

At last Joseph relented, and he sent his brothers back to Canaan, commanding his steward to fill their sacks with grain and to return their money in the sacks. But he held behind his brother Simeon in Egypt, saying that when they returned again for grain, they must bring Benjamin with them and he would then free Simeon.

The brothers journeyed back to the land of Canaan, and when they opened the sacks, there was their money which the steward had returned. They told their father all that had happened, and they were afraid in their hearts. Jacob answered them, saying, "You have taken my children from me. Joseph is not, Simeon is in Egypt, and now you would have Benjamin."

The famine continued, and at last the day came when the grain was gone. Once more Jacob said to his sons, "Go again to Egypt and buy us a little food."

When they reminded their father that Benjamin must go with them in order to win the release of Simeon, his heart was heavy with its sorrow, but the need for food was very great. "Take with you gifts for the Egyptian," he said. "Take balm and myrrh, honey, spices, nuts and almonds. Take also double your money and your brother, Benjamin. And may God in His mercy return my sons to me."

When the brothers came once more into Egypt and stood before Joseph, he still did not reveal himself to them. He set a great feast before them, showing special favor to his brother Benjamin.

But when the feast was finished and the asses loaded with grain, Joseph secretly ordered that his own silver cup should be put in the sack of grain belonging to Benjamin. As soon as the morning was light, the men set forth, but presently the head steward rode up to them and said, "One of you has stolen my master's silver cup, and he demands that the thief become his slave."

The sacks were opened up in order, beginning with the eldest brother, and behold, when the sack of Benjamin, the youngest, was opened, there was the cup.

Now were the brothers greatly troubled. They returned to Joseph's house and fell before him, begging for mercy, saying their father would surely die if they returned without their youngest brother.

Now at last did Joseph weep before his brothers. He embraced them and said, "I am he whom you sold into slavery. But be not grieved, for God sent me before you so that in the time of famine I would be here to preserve you and our people."

And Joseph forgave his brothers. He commanded that his father, Jacob, and all his family be brought to live in Egypt in the land of Goshen so that they might have food for all their days and prosper.

MOSES

For many years the Israelites were welcome in Egypt, but in time the Egyptians turned on them and made them slaves. Moses was the man chosen by God to free His people and lead them back to Canaan, the promised land.

IN EGYPT THE CHILDREN OF THE ISRAELITES grew in numbers. The land was filled with them, and they became mighty. But when a new Pharaoh, who had never known Joseph and his brothers, came to the throne, he feared the Israelites and the strength the Lord had given them. Therefore, he commanded that they become slaves of the Egyptians and that every boy baby that was born be cast into the river.

But one mother hid her baby boy for three months. When she could no longer hide him, she laid him in a small boat, made of rushes and daubed with mud, and she set him to float on the river Nile. Here he was found by Pharaoh's daughter when she came to the river to bathe. She took pity on the baby, and she ordered that he be raised as an Egyptian. She named him Moses, which means "drawn from the water."

When he had grown to manhood, Moses came upon an Egyptian beating an Israelite slave, and in his anger Moses killed him. For fear of punishment he fled the land of Egypt. But the Lord was with Moses, and He appeared to him in the wilderness in a flame of fire from a bush, but the bush was not burned. And the Lord spoke to Moses from the midst of the burning bush and said, "Go before Pharaoh so that you may lead my people back to the land of Canaan which I promised to them. Speak also to the elders of Israel, telling them that the Lord their God commands them to follow you."

And Moses answered, saying that they would not believe him. Then the Lord gave to Moses a sign, turning his rod into a serpent even as he held it in his hand. So it was that when Moses went before his people, the Lord once more caused his rod to turn into a serpent, and the people believed.

Then Moses went into the presence of Pharaoh, demanding that the children of Israel be free to return to the promised land of Canaan. But the heart of Pharaoh was hard, and to mock Moses and his God, he ordered that the Israelites make bricks without straw, even to the same number as they had made them with straw.

Now was the anger of the Lord aroused. He visited plagues upon the land of Egypt. He caused frogs to rain down and the waters to turn to blood. Locusts cursed the land, and swarms of flies. Mighty thundering and hail cut down the grain, and the cattle sickened and died. Once more Moses went before Pharaoh and said, "The Lord commands, 'Let my people go so

that they may serve Me.' " But the heart of Pharaoh was hard, and he would not listen.

Then Moses called together the elders of Israel and said, "With the blood of a newly slain lamb mark well the door frame of your houses, and stay within until morning. For this night the angel of death will come to claim the firstborn of every house in Egypt."

And so it was that there was not a house in Egypt where there was not one dead, even in the house of Pharaoh. But the angel of death passed over the houses of the Israelites, which were daubed with the blood of the lamb.

Now at last Pharaoh relented, and he ordered that the Israelites be free to leave the land of Egypt, saying, "Rise up and depart from among my people. Go serve your Lord, and take also your flocks and herds."

But once they had gone Pharaoh regretted what he had done, and he pursued them with warriors in chariots.

"Now indeed are we lost!" cried the Israelites. "Before us lie the waters of the sea and behind us come the armies of Pharaoh. Better that we had lived in Egypt as slaves than die here in the wilderness."

But Moses struck the waters of the sea with his rod, and the waters drew back so that the Israelites might pass safely out of Egypt. And when Pharaoh rode after them, the waters came together with a great rush, and the Egyptians were drowned.

Thus Moses led his people toward the land of Canaan. The Lord traveled before them in a pillar of cloud by day and a pillar of fire by night. And the Lord fed His people with manna which fell from heaven, so that the Israelites might not die in the wilderness.

THE TEN COMMANDMENTS

After freeing the Israelites from slavery, Moses continued to be their leader. Through Moses God gave His Ten Commandments to them. But the Israelites displeased God by doing wicked things, and so He made them wander for many years before they at last came back to the promised land of Canaan.

I T HAPPENED THAT THE LORD led the children of Israel near to the Mount of Sinai, which was a holy place, for the Lord was there. He commanded Moses to go up into the mountain so that He might speak to him alone. And the glory of the Lord was upon the mountain for six days in a cloud, and on the seventh day He called to Moses out of the cloud, and the sight of the glory was like a devouring fire to the eyes of the children of Israel.

For forty days and forty nights Moses stayed upon Mount Sinai, and the Lord gave him His Ten Commandments, written on stone by the finger of God. And these were the commandments of God:

I am the Lord your God. Thou shalt have no other gods before me.
Thou shalt not make any images or idols, nor bow down and worship them.
Thou shalt not use the name of the Lord for evil purposes.
Remember the sabbath day and keep it holy.
Honor thy father and thy mother.
Thou shalt not kill.
Thou shalt not commit adultery.
Thou shalt not steal.
Thou shalt not bring false charges against your fellow men.
Thou shalt not covet that which is not yours.

But now the Israelites had become impatient. They felt in their hearts that their God and Moses had left them. Therefore, they commanded Aaron, who was a priest with Moses, to make a god that they could worship. All their gold ornaments and gold earrings did they give to Aaron, and he made a golden calf for a god.

Then was the time for Moses to come down from the heights of the mountain, and when he saw the calf and the dancing of the people, in his anger he cast the tablets of the Law out of his hands and broke them upon the ground. He destroyed also the golden image, and the people trembled with fear of him.

Now was the Lord prepared to forsake His people, for they had vexed Him beyond all reason. But Moses spoke to the Lord, reminding Him of His promise to Abraham and to Jacob. And Moses pleaded that the Israelites be spared.

Then the Lord relented His anger, and He sent His people on their way to the land of Canaan, with one of His angels to lead. For forty years did the children of Israel wander in the wilderness before they could enter the promised land, for they had angered the Lord their God.

And when the days of Moses were drawing to an end, he called a man named Joshua to his side and gave him his blessing, commanding him to lead the Lord's people into the land of Canaan.

In the city of Jericho in the land of Canaan the people had shut themselves up behind its walls, for they were in great fear of the Israelites. And the Israelites marched on the city to capture it and the land of milk and honey for themselves. But Jericho was a strong fortress, and the Canaanites were safe behind its walls.

Joshua commanded that the Israelites march around the walls of Jericho for six days, while the priests of the Lord blew upon trumpets of rams' horns. Then on the seventh day, with one voice the Israelites gave a great shout, and the walls of Jericho fell down flat before them. And in such a manner did the Lord bring His children into the promised land.

SAMSON

While much of the Bible tells the history of the Israelites, their seeking after God, and their victories and defeats, there are also stories that do no more than tell of man's faith and trust in God and of God's goodness to man. Such is the story of Samson, of Shadrach, Meshach, and Abednego, of Daniel, of Esther, and of Ruth and Naomi.

THERE WAS AMONG THE ISRAELITES a man stronger than any man alive, named Samson, whom the Lord had blessed. The Lord had commanded that Samson was never to cut his hair, for that was the secret of his great strength. So great was Samson that with his bare hands he killed a young lion, and with the jawbone of an ass he slew one thousand of the Philistines, who were his enemies.

Now Samson loved a woman named Delilah, and the lords

of the Philistines came to her, promising that they would each give her a hundred pieces of silver if she could learn the secret of Samson's great strength. And so Delilah pleaded with Samson that to prove his love for her, he tell her what made him so strong. Could anything bind him and make him powerless against his enemies?

First Samson told her that if she were to bind him with seven green willow stems, he would then be as weak as any other man. But when she had bound him thus, she cried, "The Philistines are upon you, Samson," and he at once broke free.

Again she begged him to tell her the secret of his strength, and he said to her, "Bind me with new rope that has never been used before, and I will be as weak as any other man." But when Delilah bound him with new rope, he broke it like a thread.

In this way he teased her, but every day she tormented him with her question, until at last Samson told her the secret of his strength. From birth he had obeyed the Lord's command that no razor should ever touch his head.

Lulling him to sleep, Delilah sent for the Philistines, and they shaved off the seven locks of Samson's hair. Then she woke him, saying, "The Philistines are upon you!" But when he rose up to defend himself, his strength was like that of a child.

The Philistines seized him and put out his eyes and bound him with fetters of brass. Then he was condemned to grind in the prison house with slaves. In this way the Philistines gloried in their triumph over Samson.

In time the hairs once more grew on Samson's head, but the Philistines in their triumph did not notice. On a day of great celebration to their god Dagon, the Philistines cried, "Let us bring Samson to the temple so we may mock him before our god!"

When Samson was called from the mill and brought into the temple, he spoke to the young boy who was leading him and said, "Place me between the pillars which support the roof so that I may rest against them, for I am tired from my work."

While the Philistines mocked Samson and the God of Israel, Samson put his arms about the pillars and prayed to the Lord. "Remember me, O Lord God," he cried, "and strengthen me this one time that I may take revenge on my enemies for my two eyes."

Then Samson bowed himself with all his might against the pillars of the temple with his arms. "Let me die with the Philistines," he cried, and with a roar the roof of the temple crashed down upon the worshipers of Dagon. And the number that Samson killed at his death was greater than all he had killed in his life.

SHADRACH, MESHACH, AND ABEDNEGO

AT THE TIME WHEN THE BABYLONIANS RULED over the children of Israel, there was a king named Nebuchadnezzar. He had made a statue of gold ninety feet high and nine feet wide, and he set it up on a great plain. Then he gathered together all the princes and governors, the captains and judges of his kingdom to stand in wonder before the golden statue. The king's herald cried aloud to them, "Whenever you hear the sound of the harp and flute, the cornet and dulcimer and all manner of music, it is commanded that you bow down to the image and worship it. All those who do not do this shall be cast into a burning furnace."

So it was that when the music was heard, everyone bowed down to the golden image and worshiped it. But among the people there were three Jews named Shadrach, Meshach, and Abednego who would not bow down to the image, for they worshiped only God.

When Nebuchadnezzar heard of this, in his fury he commanded that Shadrach, Meshach, and Abednego be brought to him. The king questioned the three men, saying, "Is it true that you serve not my gods, nor worship the golden image? I order

41

you — bow down to the image when you hear the sound of the harp and flute and the cornet and dulcimer, and all will be well. If not, you will be thrown into the middle of a burning furnace, and who is the god who will save you?"

Then Shadrach, Meshach, and Abednego answered the king: "We do not need to answer. If it be His will, our God whom we serve will deliver us from the furnace and from your hands. But if it is not His will, we still cannot serve your gods, O King, or worship your golden image."

Nebuchadnezzar was filled with fury, and he gave orders that the furnace be made seven times hotter. Then the strongest men of his army bound up Shadrach, Meshach, and Abednego, and when the three were cast into the furnace, those who cast them were consumed by its great heat.

When the king looked into the furnace, he was astonished, for he saw not three men but four men walking about in the flames, and the fourth man was the angel of the Lord. The heart of Nebuchadnezzar was moved, and he called Shadrach, Meshach, and Abednego out of the furnace. Behold, not a hair of their heads was singed, nor were their clothes burned, and there was no smell of fire about them.

Then Nebuchadnezzar spoke before his people and said, "Blessed be the God of Shadrach, Meshach, and Abednego, who has sent His angel to save these men who trusted Him from the fire. Therefore, I order that any man who says anything against this God shall be cut to pieces, and his house shall become a dumping ground."

And Shadrach, Meshach, and Abednego were respected by the king, and they were given positions of high honor in the kingdom of Babylon.

RUTH
AND NAOMI

IN THE DAYS when the Judges ruled Israel, there was a famine in the land. A certain man named Elimelech, who lived in Bethlehem, in Judah, went with his wife, Naomi, and their two sons to live in the country of Moab, because there was food in that land.

In time Elimelech, Naomi's husband, died, and her two sons took wives. They were women of Moab, and the name of one was Orpah, and the name of the other was Ruth. And Naomi and her sons and their wives lived in Moab for about ten years.

It came to pass that both sons died. Naomi was alone in a strange land with her daughters-in-law. She now prepared to return to her own country, for she heard that there was once more food in the land of Judah. Orpah and Ruth set out with Naomi to see that she was well started on her journey. At last it was time for them to part, and Naomi said to her daughters-in-law, "Return now each of you to your mother's house. May the Lord be as kind to you as you have been to me and to my sons."

The women wept together, and Orpah returned to her moth-

er's house. But Ruth clung to Naomi and said, "Do not ask me to leave you. Wherever you go, I shall go; where you stop, there will I stop also. Your people shall be my people, and your God shall be my God."

Naomi, seeing that she could not persuade Ruth to go back, permitted her to continue on to Bethlehem.

It was the time of the barley harvest, and Ruth said, "Let me go into the fields that I may follow after the reapers and glean the ears of grain which they have passed over. In this way we will have food to eat."

It happened that Ruth was gleaning in a field that belonged to a wealthy kinsman of Naomi's named Boaz. When Boaz saw Ruth, he asked his servants who she was. The servant replied that she was Ruth, who had returned with Naomi from the country of Moab.

Then Boaz spoke to Ruth, for she had found favor in his eyes. He told her that she might glean freely from his fields and drink the water from his well. And he instructed the servants to let her glean even among the sheaves of gathered barley and to let grain fall on the ground so that she would find enough.

When Ruth returned that night to Naomi, she told her what had happened between her and Boaz, and Naomi was joyful, for Boaz was a kinsman. So it was throughout all the barley harvest and the wheat harvest. Ruth gleaned every day with the maidservants of Boaz.

At last when the harvest was done, Boaz went before the elders of the city and declared his wish to make Ruth his wife, and the elders blessed the marriage.

And the son of Ruth and Boaz was Obed, and his son was Jesse, the father of David.

DANIEL

URING THE REIGN OF KING DARIUS a servant of the Lord named Daniel was raised up by his king to a position of high honor. Even though Daniel was of the captive nation of Judah, his wisdom and understanding were so great that Darius placed him over all the princes and lords of his kingdom. So excellent was the spirit that was within Daniel that the king preferred him above all others.

Now the princes and lords were jealous of Daniel's power, and they sought ways to humble him in the eyes of their king, but there was nothing but good in the man, and they could do nothing. Finding no evil in Daniel, they sought to find wrong in the laws of his God.

So the princes and lords came before the king and spoke. "King Darius, live forever. We have consulted among ourselves and we request that you make a royal decree. For thirty days no man shall ask a favor of any god or man. Only to you shall such favors be asked. Any man who disobeys this decree shall be cast into a den of lions."

To please his princes and lords, the king made such a decree and sealed it with his ring, knowing that according to the laws of the Medes and Persians, such a decree could not be changed.

When Daniel learned of this writing, he went into his chamber, and going to the window that faced toward Jerusalem, he knelt and prayed as was his practice three times a day, giving praise and thanks to his God.

Then the princes and lords came upon Daniel making supplication to his God, and they went before Darius and reminded him of his decree, saying, "Even now Daniel kneels three times a day to petition his God according to the laws of the Jews. Will you not have him cast into the den of lions according to your decree which cannot be changed under the law of the Medes and Persians?"

The heart of the king was sore when he heard these words, for he loved Daniel, and throughout the day he pondered how he might save him. With the setting of the sun the princes and lords came again to Darius to remind him once more of his decree. Then the king commanded that Daniel be brought before him and cast into the den of lions. He spoke and said, "Surely your God, whom you serve, will deliver you." And he set the seal of his ring on the rock which covered the door of the den.

That night there was no sound of music in the palace. No food was set before the king, and his eyes did not close with

sleep, so great was his concern for Daniel. Then early in the morning Darius rose up and hurried to the den of lions. "O Daniel," he cried out, "servant of the living God. Was your God able to save you from the lions' jaws?"

And Daniel answered, saying, "O King, live forever. My God has sent His angel to shut the mouths of the lions, for in His sight I am innocent, and to you, O King, I have done no harm."

Then did the king rejoice. He ordered his seal to be broken and the rock rolled away so that Daniel could walk out of the den. And no mark was found on him, for the lions had not touched him.

Now the king commanded that the princes and lords who had accused Daniel, and their wives and children also, should be thrown into the den. And the lions broke their bones.

King Darius wrote a new decree in all the languages of his kingdom so that all men would know it. "I command that in every part of my kingdom men shall tremble before the God of Daniel, who saved him from the wrath of the lions. He is the living God, and His kingdom shall not be destroyed."

And thus Daniel prospered in the reign of Darius the Mede and in the reign of Cyrus the Persian.

ESTHER

Now in the days when the Jews were the captives of their enemies, they were ruled by a powerful king named Ahasuerus. His rule was of the Medes and Persians, and so great was his kingdom that it stretched from Ethiopia even to the land of India. He sat upon his throne in the palace in Shushan, where there were white, green and blue hangings, fastened with cords of fine linen and purple to silver rings and pillars of marble.

There was a certain Jew named Mordecai. He was one of the palace guards, and he sat outside the gates. He had brought up his uncle's daughter, Esther, as his own because she had neither mother nor father.

It came to pass that the king wished to have a queen. Esther pleased the king above all women, and he took her into the palace for his wife, placing a crown of gold on her head so that she might be queen. And Mordecai counseled her not to reveal herself or her people to the king.

On a certain day, as Mordecai sat by the palace gates, he heard two of the king's chamberlains plotting to do the king harm. This did Mordecai tell to Esther, and she repeated it to the king, saying that it was Mordecai who had told her. When it was found to be true, the chamberlains were hanged from a tree, and the king put a man named Haman in their place, above all the princes of the land. Now when Haman walked about, all bowed low to him, as the king had commanded. But Mordecai, the Jew, would not bow down to Haman or show him respect.

Haman was filled with anger, and he wished not only Mordecai but all the Jews in the kingdom to be killed. He went before the king, Ahasuerus, and said to him that among his people there were certain ones who were different, and they obeyed only their own laws and not the king's. "If it please the king," he said, "let there be a decree that they are to be destroyed, and all their wealth seized for your treasury."

The king did as Haman had requested. In the king's name it was written that on such-and-such a day all Jews were to be slain and their wealth given over to the king's treasury. And he gave his ring to Haman so that the decree could be sealed in the king's name.

Then through all the land was the law sent out, sealed with the king's own ring by Haman's hand, that on such-and-such a day the people were to rise up and strike down all the Jews, taking unto the king's treasury all their wealth.

So great was Mordecai's sorrow when he heard the decree pronounced that he tore his clothes and dressed himself in sackcloth and ashes. He went about the city and cried with a loud and bitter cry, even before the gates of the palace.

The lament of the Jews was heard throughout the land, and presently her maidservants brought word of it to Queen Esther. She sent her chamberlain to Mordecai to ask him the reason for it. Mordecai told him all that had happened. The king through Haman had decreed the death of all the Jews. And Mordecai said that Esther must go before the king and plead

with him to the chamberlain for the lives of her people.

The chamberlain told her of this, and she replied, "No one may go before the king on pain of death unless he summons. The king has not called me to come to him in thirty days. Go tell this to Mordecai."

When the chamberlain had done this, Mordecai answered that not even Esther, the queen, would be safe from the king's decree. Perhaps she was meant to be the instrument of the Lord to save His people.

The chamberlain gave her Mordecai's answer, and she sent him back once again. "Tell him to gather together all the Jews in Shushan. Have them fast for me. Let them eat or drink nothing for three days, neither night nor day. I and my maidens will fast also. Then I will go unbidden before the king. If I perish, I perish."

On the third day Esther put on her royal raiment and went and stood in the inner court of the king's palace. And when he saw her, she found favor in his eyes. He held out his golden scepter so that she might approach him without harm. "What will you have, Queen Esther?" he said. "What is your request? It shall be given to you, even to half my kingdom."

"If it please you, my king," she replied. "Let you and Haman come this day to a banquet I have prepared for you. And on the morrow you will come again to my table, and at that time I will speak my request."

And the king so ordered, telling Haman to make haste to come into the queen's presence. Then verily Haman was puffed up with pride, and he feasted with King Ahasuerus and his queen on the first day.

But as he hurried from the palace to tell his wife and friends of his good fortune, he passed Mordecai at the gate, and Mordecai did not bow down to him. His heart was filled with hatred, and after telling his wife and his friends about the banquet, he said, "Yet all of this is as nothing in my sight so long as Mordecai, the Jew, will not bow down to me." And he ordered a gallows fifty cubits high, on which to hang his enemy.

The second day was like the first, and when the feasting was done, the king turned again to Esther, saying, "What is your request that I may grant it, even to half my kingdom?"

Then Esther, the queen, answered, "If I have found favor in your sight, O King, let my life be spared and my people saved. For we are sold, my people and I, to be destroyed, to be slain and to perish."

Then the king rose up in his anger and said, "Who is it that presumes in his heart to do so?"

And Esther said, "The enemy of my people is this wicked Haman."

Now, indeed, was Haman fearful for his life before the king and queen, and he threw himself on the queen's couch to beg for mercy, but the king's wrath was too great. He ordered that Haman be hanged fifty cubits high, even on the gallows that had been prepared for Mordecai.

Then King Ahasuerus sent out orders throughout his kingdow that the Jews were to be spared, and he raised up Mordecai high in his court, giving unto him the ring of gold which had been Haman's. And he dressed him in royal robes of blue and white, with a golden crown for his head, while the city of Shushan rejoiced.

And thus it was that Queen Esther brought about the salvation of her people.

DAVID
AND GOLIATH

One of the greatest Kings of Israel was David. He was a simple shepherd boy who loved the Lord, and God chose him to be ruler over the Israelites. The lovely poems which we call the Psalms are believed to have been written by King David. The story of how David, the shepherd boy, killed the mighty giant, Goliath, is one of the most famous stories in the Bible.

A T THE TIME WHEN SAUL was King of the Israelites, their enemies, the Philistines, had gathered a great army to battle against Israel. The Philistines camped on the side of a mountain, the Israelites on another mountain, with a valley between them. And the armies together numbered in the thousands.

56

But there was with the Philistines a mighty man, a giant of nine feet and nine inches, named Goliath, and all the Israelites feared him greatly, for he was a mighty warrior. He was girded with a coat of mail, and a helmet of brass sat upon his head, and he was armed with a spear of great weight and a shield of brass also.

When the armies were drawn up to do battle, Goliath came out and taunted the Israelites, saying, "Send me your bravest soldier and let him fight with me alone. If he can fight with me and kill me, then we will be your slaves. But if I kill him, then shall you be our slaves."

When King Saul and his men heard these words, their fear was very great. No man among them was brave enough to fight with Goliath. And every morning and every evening for forty days Goliath taunted the Israelites.

Meantime, a young shepherd boy named David was at home tending the sheep of his father, Jesse, while his three brothers were with the army of Saul. Jesse said to his son, "Take this food to the camp of King Saul, and seek out your brothers so that they may eat it." And David did as his father commanded, leaving his sheep in the care of a keeper.

It came to pass that while David was talking with his brothers, Goliath came forth and again challenged the Israelites to fight him. David said, "Who is this heathen Philistine that he should taunt the army of the Living God?" But his brothers gave him no heed, saying that he should be home tending his father's sheep.

It happened that David's words were repeated to King Saul, and the king sent for the boy so that he might speak to him. David answered his king and said, "Be not afraid, for I will

fight this Philistine. He has challenged the armies of the Living God, and the Lord who has protected me, even from the lion that would slay my sheep, will watch over me now when I do battle with Goliath."

Then Saul gave the boy his blessing, and David was dressed in armor. But the shield, the helmet of brass, and the spear weighed heavily upon his shoulders, and he put it off. So he went forth to meet Goliath clad only in his shepherd's tunic, armed with a sling and five smooth pebbles from the brook, and he drew near to the Philistine.

When Goliath saw the boy approach, he scorned him and said, "Am I a dog that you come to fight me with sticks? I will cut you up and give you to the birds and beasts to devour."

And David answered, "You come forth armed with a sword and spear and a shield of shining brass, but I am armed with the Lord of Hosts, the God of the armies of Israel."

Then as the Philistine rose up to strike him down, David ran toward the armies of the enemy. He fitted a pebble in his shepherd's sling and hurled it at Goliath. The stone struck the giant in the forehead, and it sank in deep so that he fell dead upon his face. With Goliath's own sword did David cut off his head and he held it up high for all to see. When the Philistines saw the death of their champion, they fled, and great was the triumph of the army of the Lord's people over their enemies.

THE HUNDREDTH PSALM

Make a joyful noise unto the Lord, all ye lands.

Serve the Lord with gladness: come before his presence with singing.

Know ye that the Lord he is God; it is he that hath made us, and not we ourselves; we are his people, and the sheep of his pasture.

Enter into his gates with thanksgiving, and into his courts with praise: be thankful unto him, and bless his name.

For the Lord is good; his mercy is everlasting; and his truth endureth to all generations.

About The Author

ALVIN TRESSELT is the author of more than twenty-five books for boys and girls, including one Caldecott winner, *White Snow, Bright Snow,* and two Caldecott runners-up. He has also co-authored books, edited collections, and contributed stories to *Humpty Dumpty* magazine, where he was editor for twelve years. At present, he is executive editor and vice-president of Parents Magazine Press.

Alvin Tresselt and his wife, Blossom, live in Redding, Connecticut. They have two daughters, Ellen and India. In addition to his writing, Alvin Tresselt's great interests are tropical fish, gardening, and collecting antiques and baroque music.

About The Artist

LYND WARD was born in Chicago, Illinois. He attended schools in Illinois, Massachusetts, and New Jersey and was graduated from Teachers College at Columbia University, where he was editor of the *Columbia Jester*. After graduation, he traveled in Europe and studied at the National Academy for Graphic Arts, Leipzig, Germany. He studied etching with Alois Kolb, lithography with Georg Mathey, woodcut with Hans Alexander Mueller.

Lynd Ward has illustrated more than 100 books, including 15 books by his wife, May McNeer. He received the Caldecott Award for *The Biggest Bear*, which he wrote as well as illustrated. He works in a wide variety of media, and his prints are in many permanent collections, including the Smithsonian Institution and the Newark Museum.

The Wards live in Cresskill, New Jersey, in the winter, and summer at Echo Bay, Ontario. They have two daughters and three grandchildren.